In memory o
Cassandra E

Author : Teresa Anderson
co Author; Edward Anderson

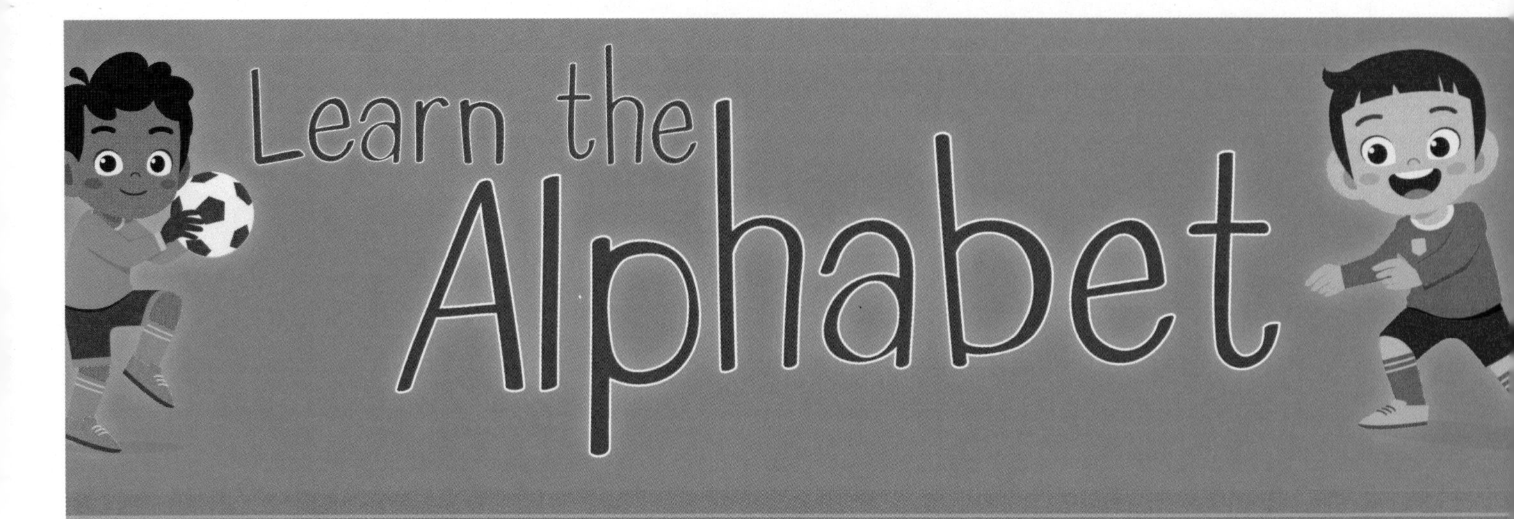

A is for...

Athletic

Learn the Alphabet

B is for...

Brave

Learn the Alphabet

C is for...

Chuckle

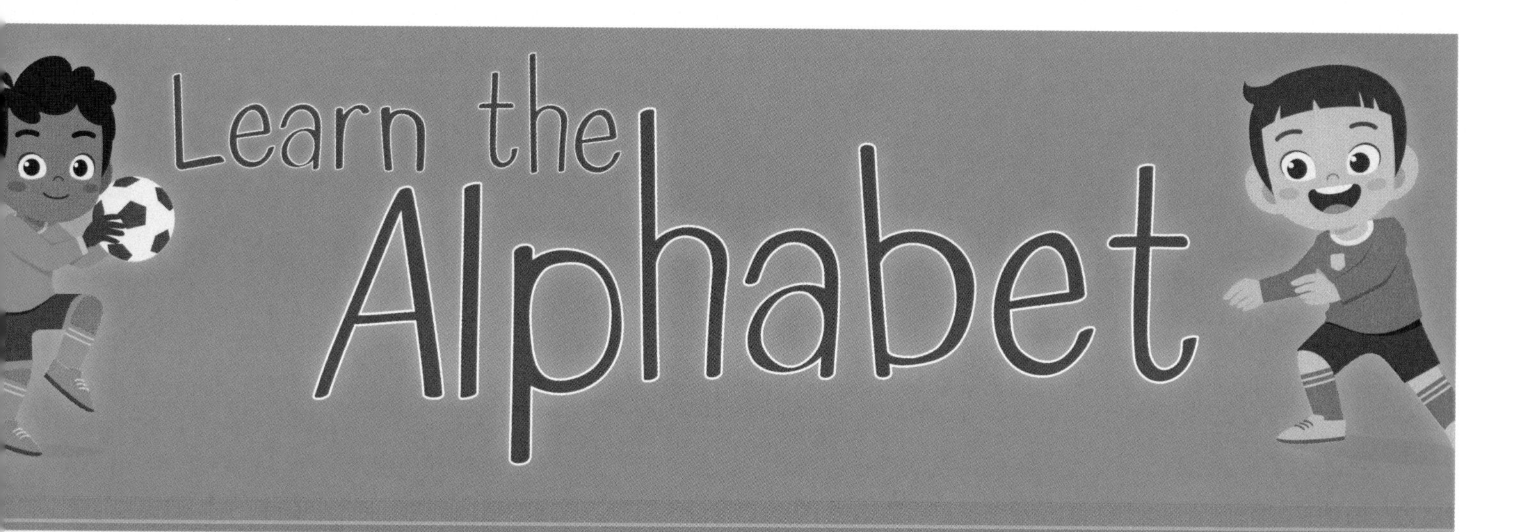

D is for...

Discover

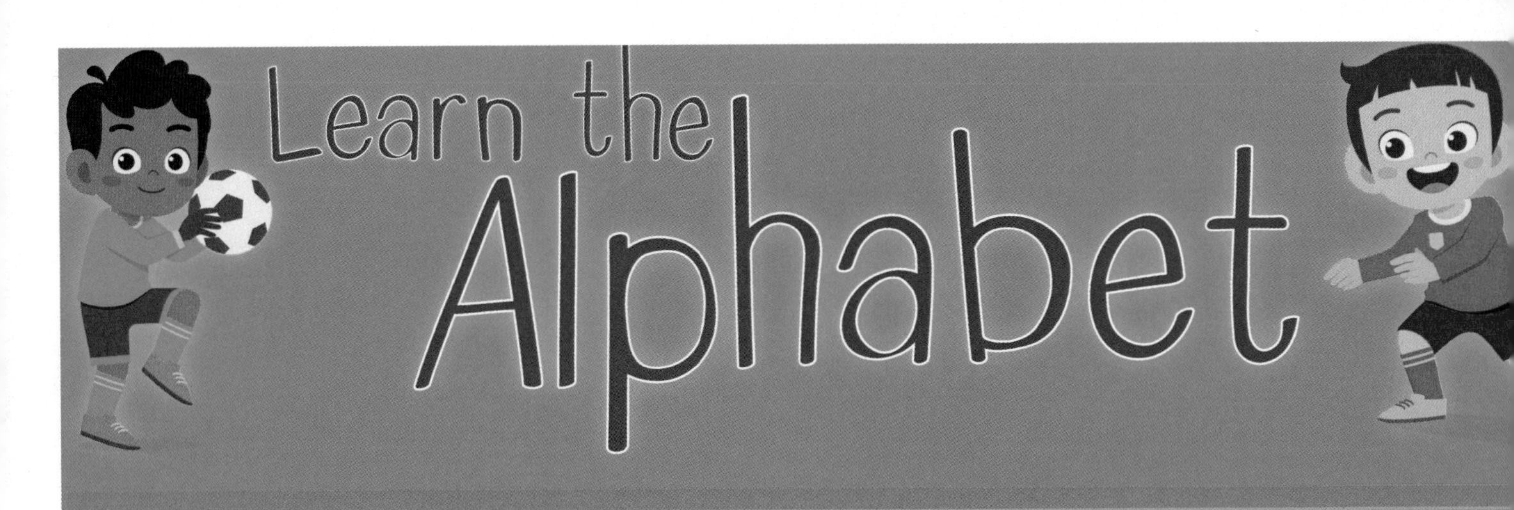

E is for...

Embrace

Learn the Alphabet

F is for...

Friends

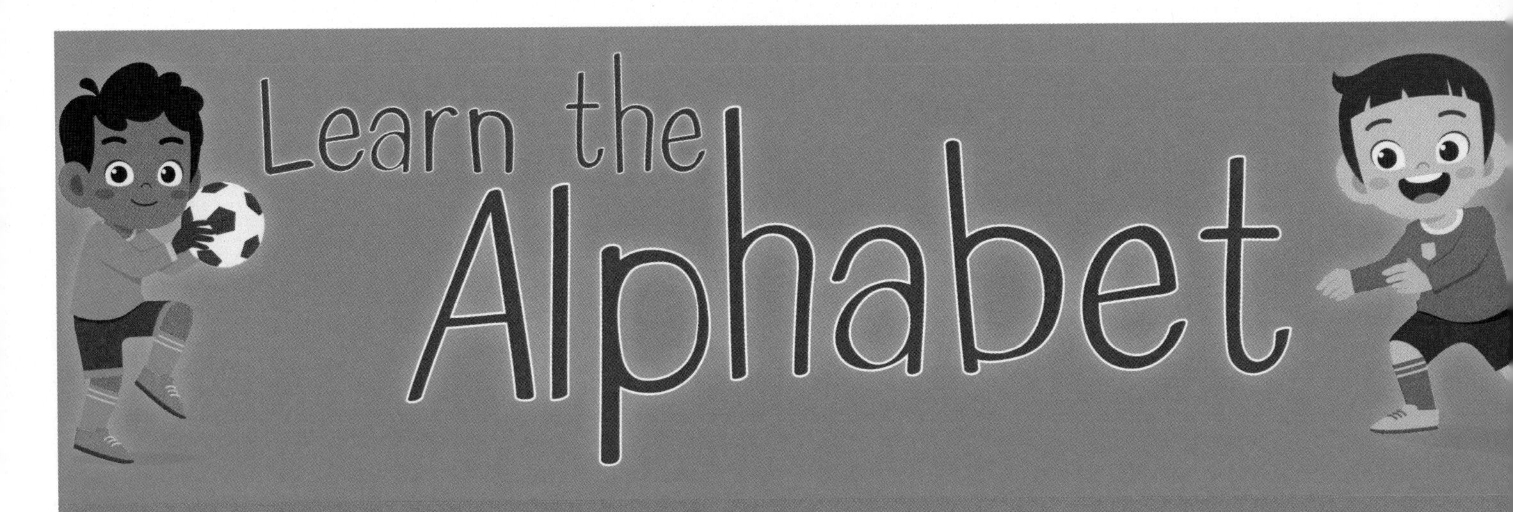

G is for...

God

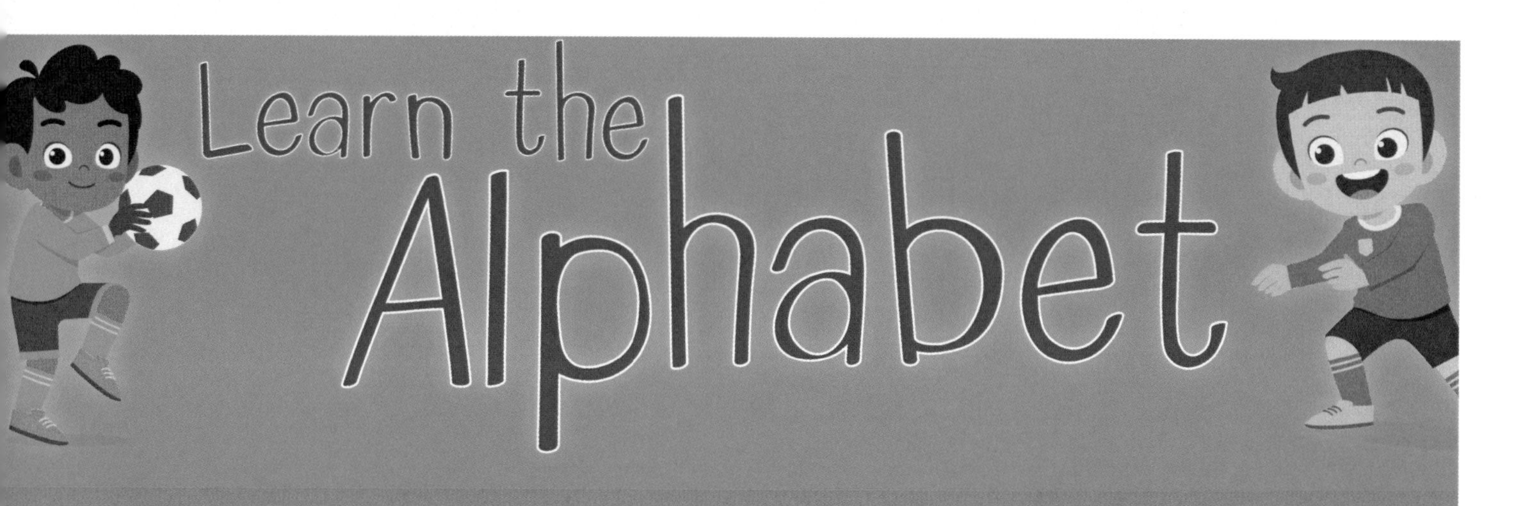

H is for...

Help

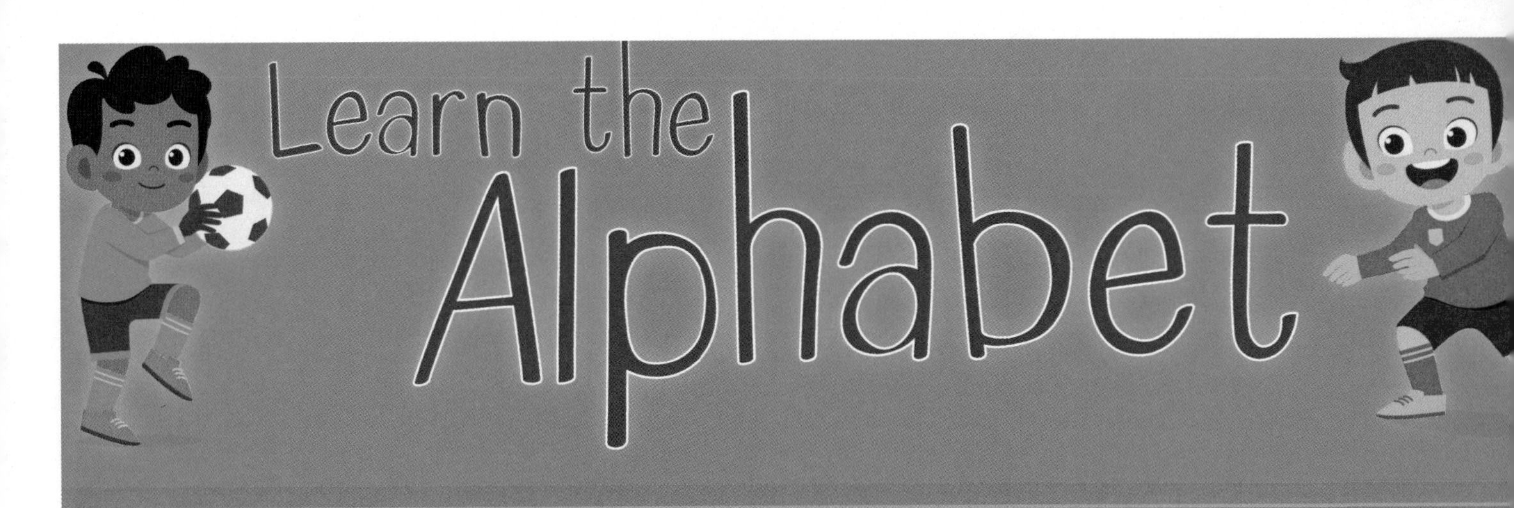

I is for...

Intelligent

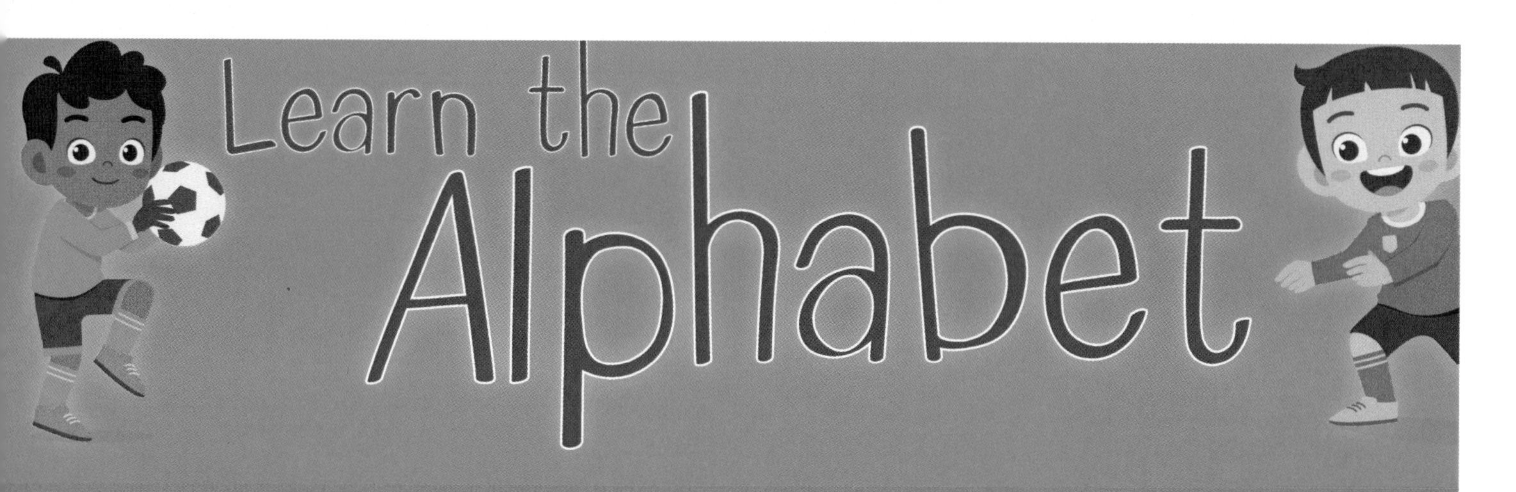

J is for...

Jumping

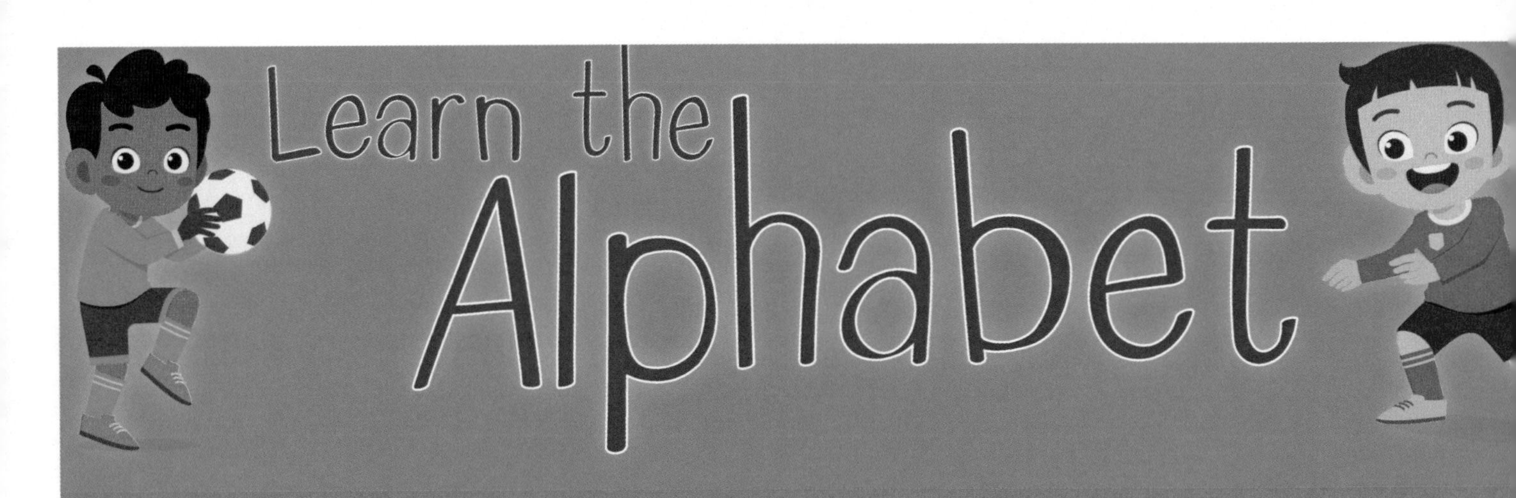

K is for...

Kickball

Learn the Alphabet

L is for...

Leader

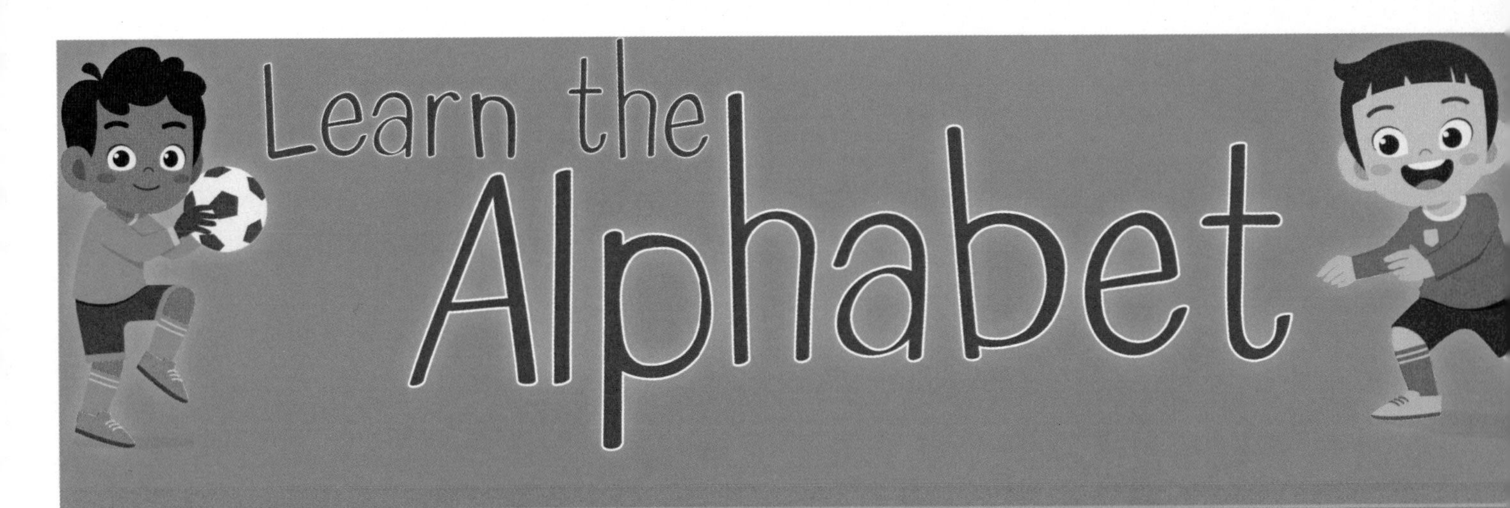
Learn the
Alphabet

M is for...

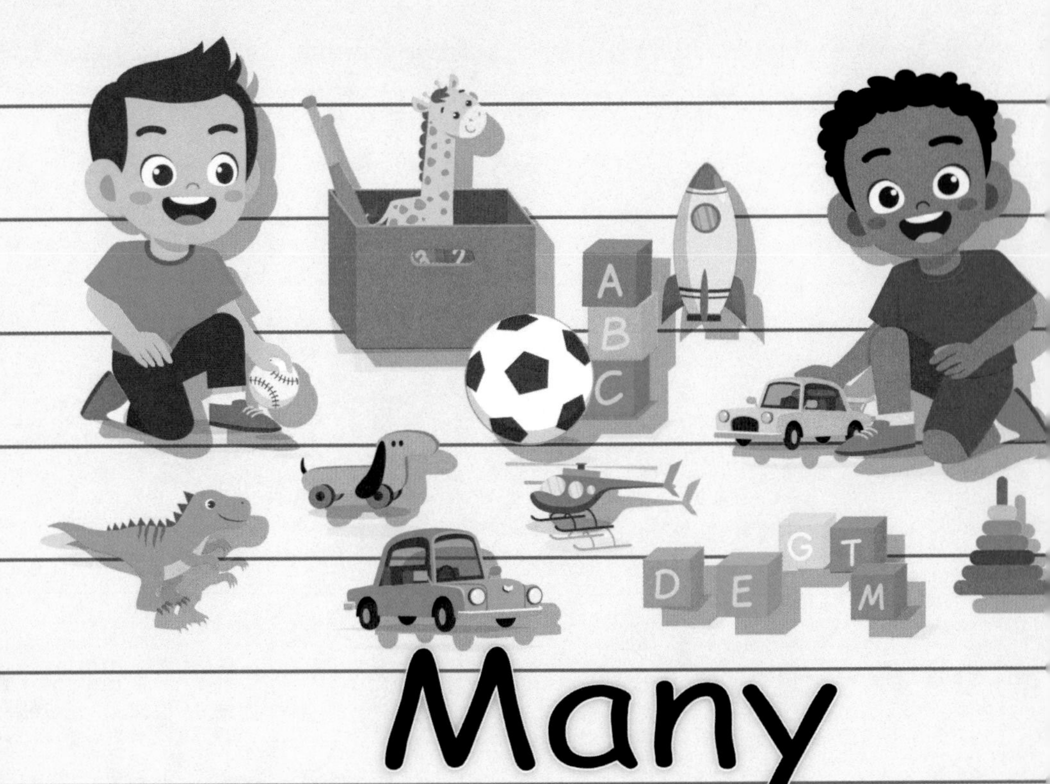
A
B
C
D
E
G
T
M

Many

Learn the Alphabet

N is for...

Now

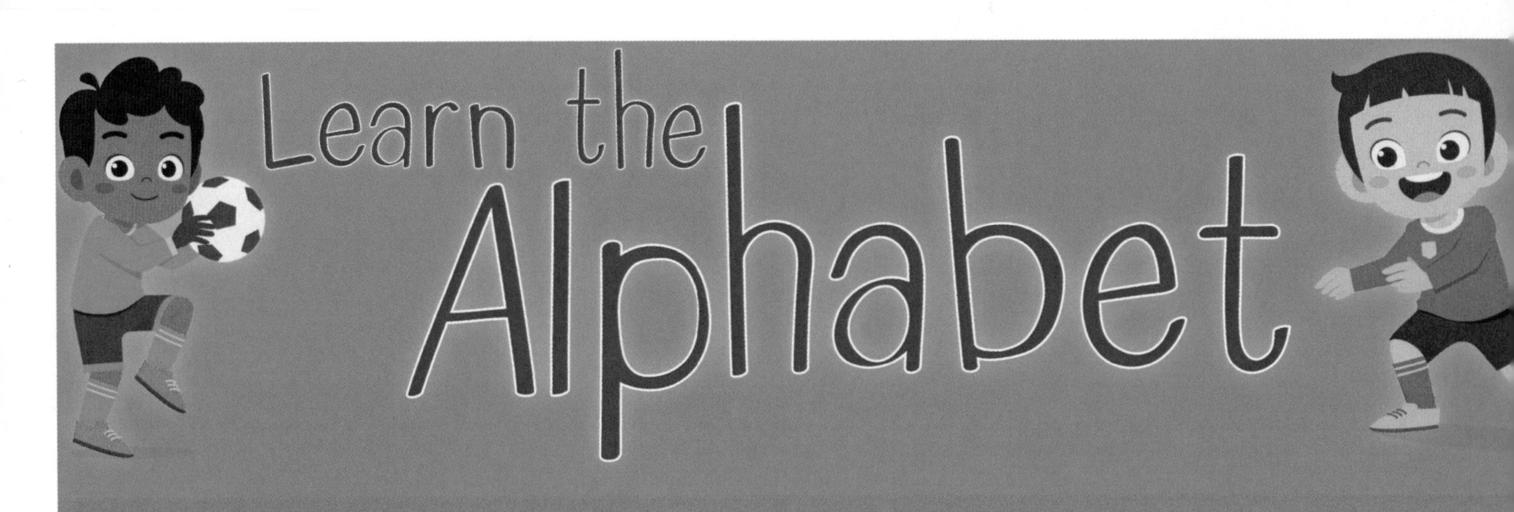

O is for...

Outgoing

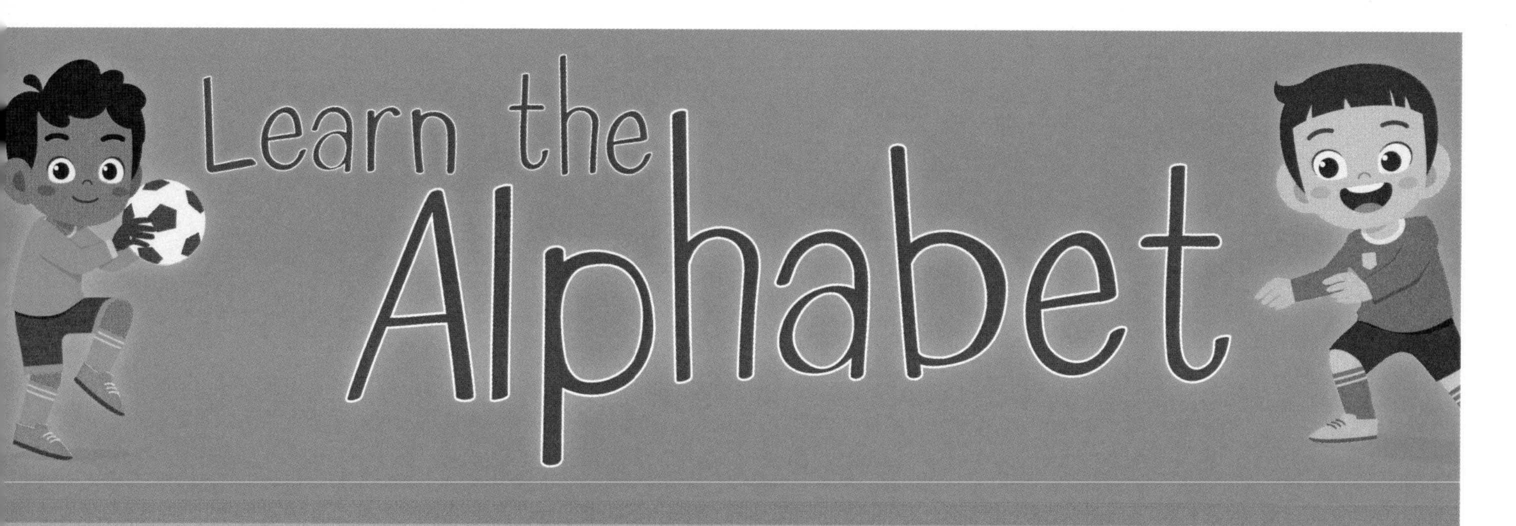

P is for...

Pet

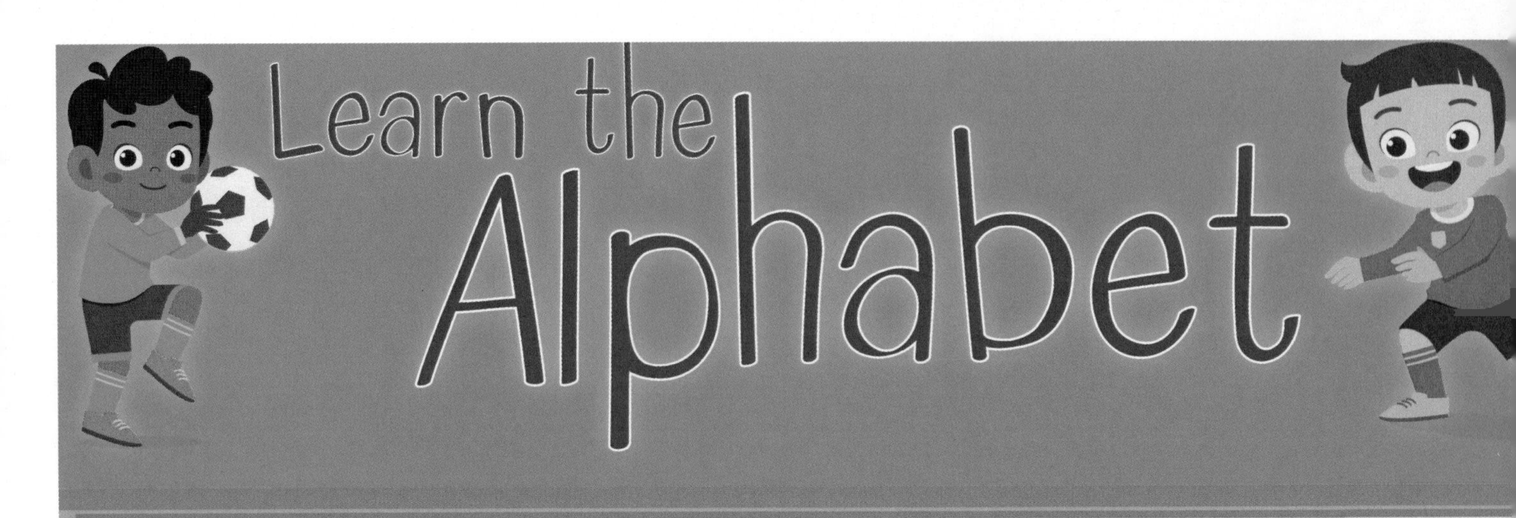

Q is for...

Quiet

Learn the Alphabet

R is for...

Reptile

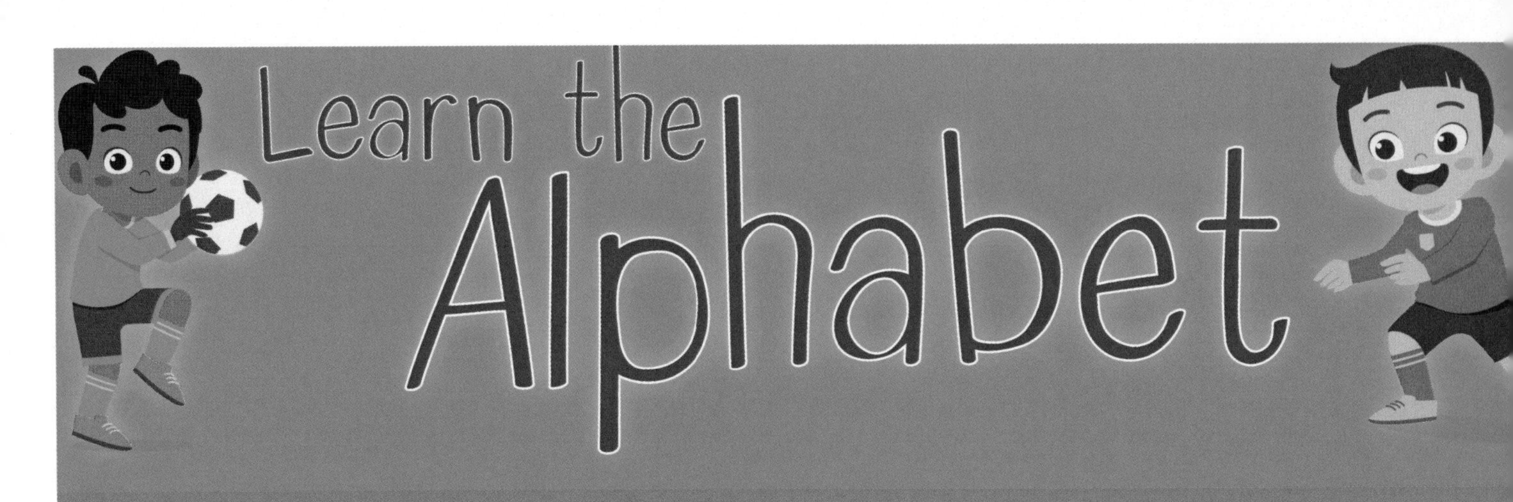

S is for...

Sunny

Learn the Alphabet

T is for...

Team

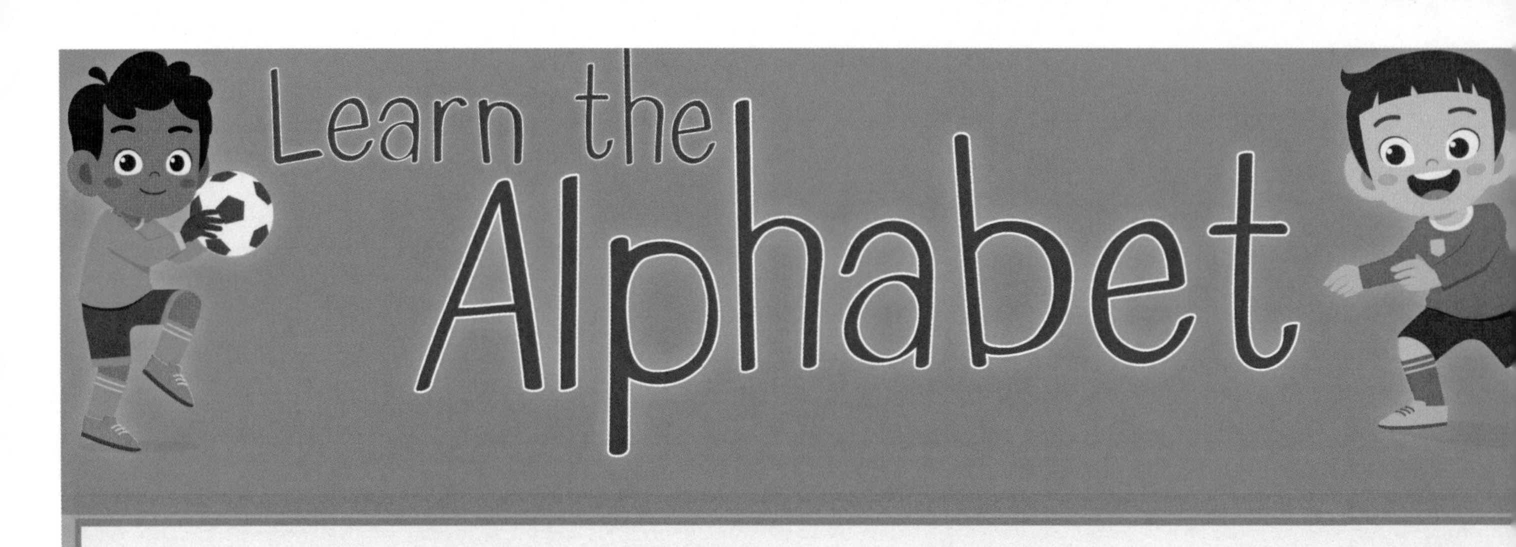

U is for...

Up

V is for...

Victory

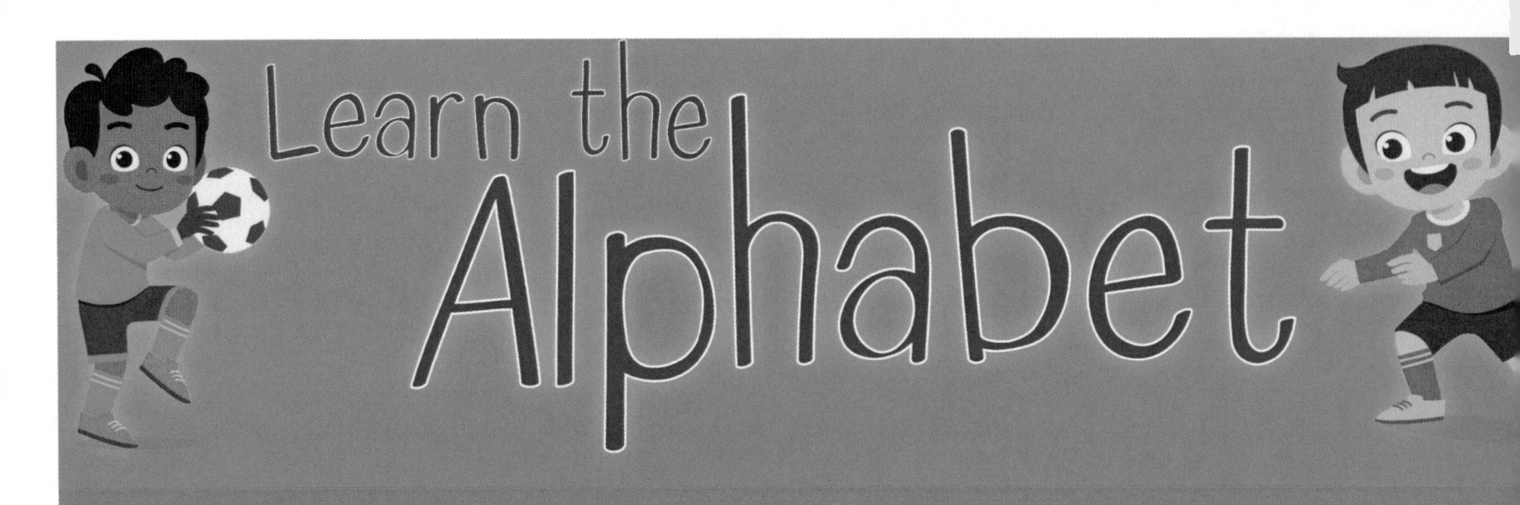

W is for...

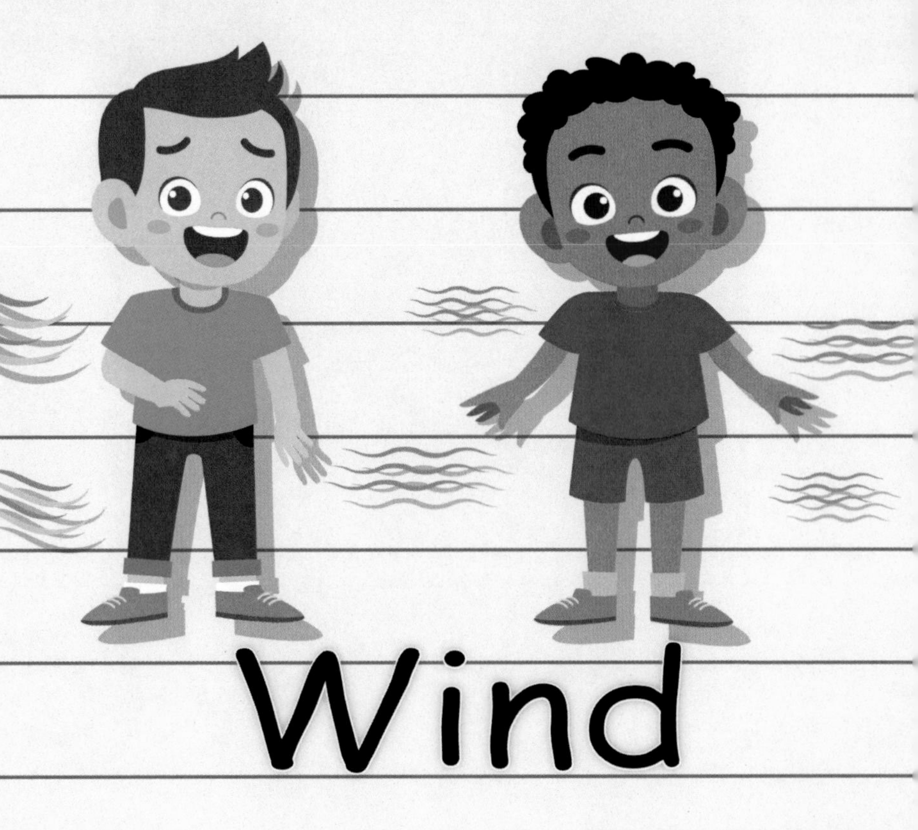

Wind

X is for...

X-ray

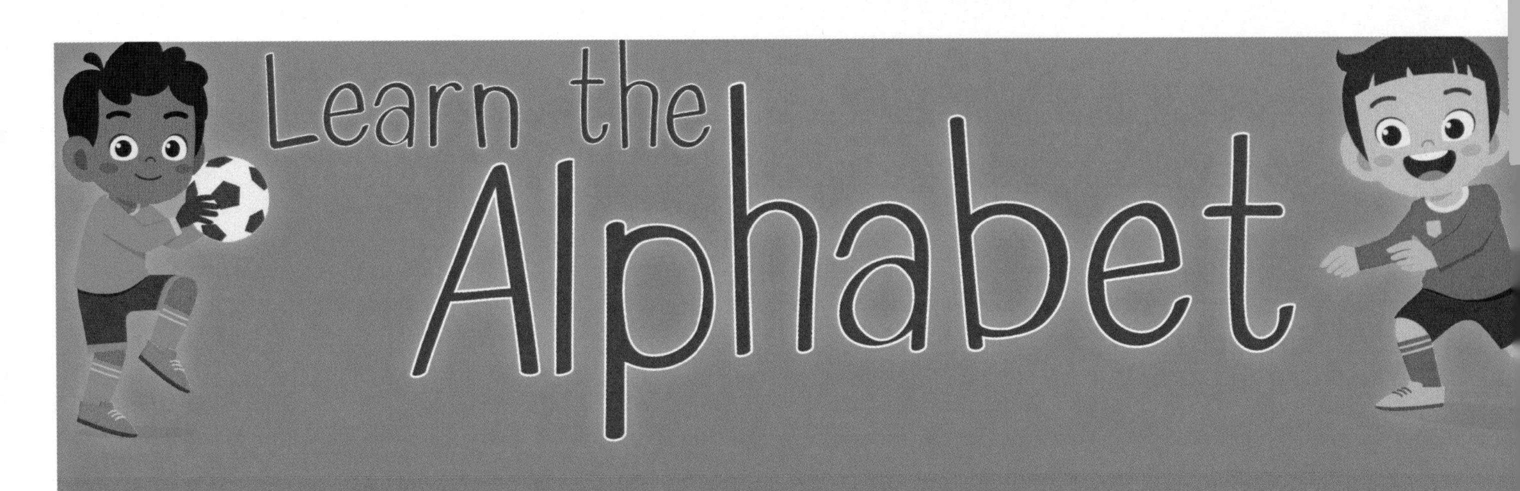

Y is for...

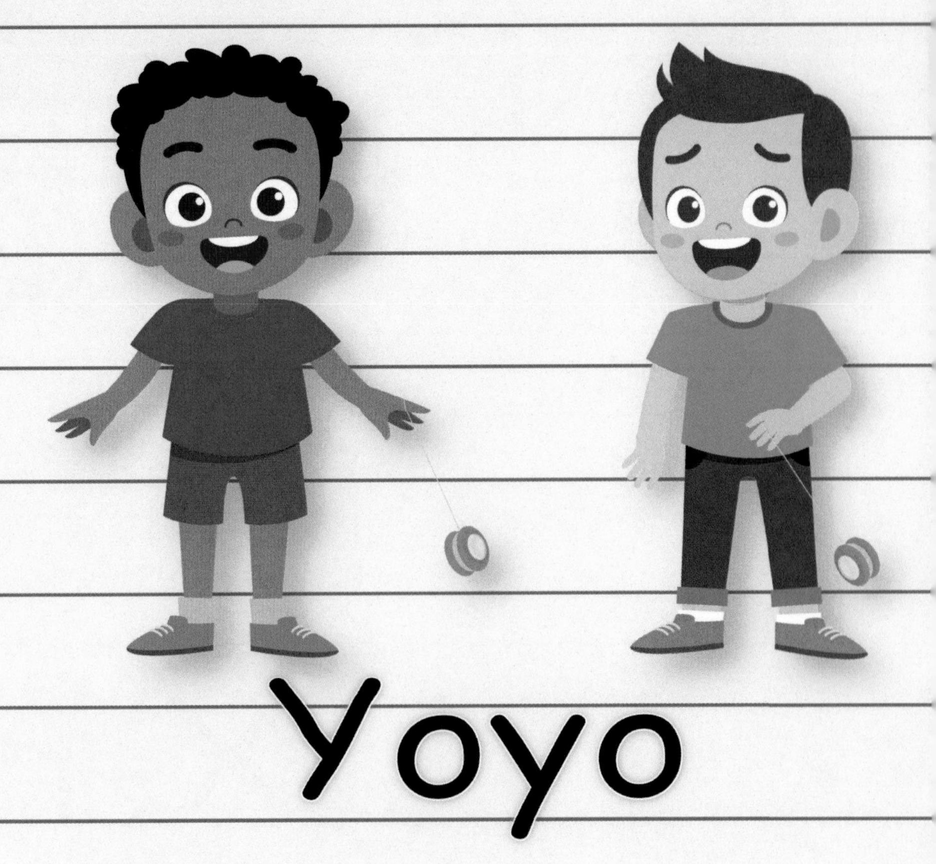

Yoyo

Learn the Alphabet

Z is for...

Zebra

Made in the USA
Middletown, DE
22 May 2022